Haddon Sundblom, 1961

TO _____

FROM _____

RECORD YOUR FAVORITE HOLIDAY MEMORIES IN A SPECIAL SECTION AT THE END OF THE BOOK.

CLEMENT C. MOORE

'Twas

THE NIGHT BEFORE CHRISTMAS

Dear Reader

The book *'Twas the Night Before Christmas* has been a mainstay of our family's holiday traditions as long as I can remember. Every Christmas Eve, we would put on our pajamas and go into our living room. We would take out our stockings and hang them with care on the mantel above our fireplace. Then we would pile onto the sofa, where my mother would read the story. My father usually was moving around the room so he could find a good vantage point for a photo or two.

After the reading of *'Twas the Night Before Christmas*, we always would make sure to leave a full glass of milk, Christmas cookies, and a note for Santa thanking him for visiting us. We would race off to bed so that Santa could come as quickly as possible. Christmas Eve night always seemed like the longest night of the year, because there was so much expectation and hope that it was clearly a long winter's nap.

My sister and brother and I always giggled about the notion of a kerchief and cap. We thought it was very silly to go to bed wearing a hat. I never was certain what visions of sugarplums dancing in my head were, but occasionally I would slip out of bed and look out the window to see if I could catch a glimpse of Santa and eight reindeer. The book gave such wonderful imagery of Santa, the sleigh, the sack of toys, and the magic of Christmas.

The tradition continues. My wife reads *'Twas the Night Before Christmas* every Christmas Eve to our children, just as my mother did for us. Sometimes we even read it a second time. We still carefully hang the stockings, put on our pajamas, and leave milk, cookies, and a note for Santa. Our daughter has added a new tradition--we now also leave carrots for the reindeer.

HADDON SUNDBLOM, 1961

I believe every Christmas of my life has involved reading *'Twas the Night Before Christmas*. Each time we read it, I'm filled with the joy of our Christmas together— the magic, the surprise, and the expectation. It also conjures up great memories of Christmas holidays from long ago. It connects me to my childhood, my parents, my grandparents, wife, and children. I have no doubt it will continue to be a tradition for my grandchildren.

All of us at Hallmark are delighted to share this timeless Christmas story with your family. We hope you will find it as special as we do. Best Wishes and Happy Holidays from our family to yours.

Don Hall Jr

DON HALL, JR.

A TRIBUTE TO
THE COCA-COLA SANTA

In 1930, famed Chicago commercial illustrator Haddon Sundblom painted a jolly, red-garbed Santa Claus for The Coca-Cola Company's 1931 Christmas advertising campaign, beginning a tradition that continues to this day. Sundblom may not have realized it at the time, but his depictions of the Coca-Cola Santa, issued annually from 1931 to 1964, formed America's perception of what Santa Claus looks like. Prior to that time, the image of Santa in the United States varied as widely as its melting-pot immigrants' memories of Father Christmas from their native countries. American Santas were sometimes shown as tall and thin, and other times as short and wizened, clad in a rainbow of colors and styles.

COCA-COLA SANTA, 1931

COCA-COLA SANTA, 1943

While Sundblom's style varied slightly over the years, the Coca-Cola Santa images always had a characteristic warmth

COCA-COLA SANTA, 1944

and charm. They incorporated elements reflective of the times—during the 1930s, dolls resembling child actress Shirley Temple appeared in the toy sack; during World War II, war bonds were displayed. Regardless of the era, Sundblom's Coca-Cola Santa consistently had the ability to draw the viewer

COCA-COLA SANTA, 1963

into the scene and express the joyousness of a season best celebrated with family. Most enchanting was Sundblom's knack for showing the Coca-Cola Santa as more than just a toy delivery-man. The Coca-Cola Santa

was also a participant in the holiday festivities—a big kid, in fact—as he raided the refrigerator, played with the toys, and always, of course, refreshed himself with an ice-cold Coca-Cola.

This endearingly childlike quality has surely contributed to the enduring appeal of the images.

Although Sundblom painted his last Coca-Cola Santa for

COCA-COLA SANTA, 1964

the 1964 Christmas season, The Coca-Cola Company still uses the Coca-Cola Santa year after year in its holiday advertising and packaging. We are honored to have made this contribution to the American holiday tradition, and look forward to sharing this cherished legacy with the world for many years to come. ■

Phillip F. Mooney
Director, Archives Department
The Coca-Cola Company

Introduction

New York City-born Clement Clarke Moore (1779-1863) was a biblical scholar, a professor of Asian and Greek literature, an author, and a man who could converse in almost any language; but he is remembered as the person who first named Santa's reindeer. While much of his scholarly work is forgotten, a poem written as a holiday gift for his children has endured as one of the most beloved pieces of Christmas literature.

What was originally entitled *A Visit From St. Nicholas* first gained public exposure in 1823 when a member of Moore's family submitted it to the *Troy Sentinel*. The newspaper published it as an anonymous work. The poem eventually became known as *'Twas the Night Before Christmas* after its opening line. Its popularity and charm initiated the paper's tradition of reprinting the work each holiday season.

By combining elements of the Dutch St. Nicholas Day holiday with American yuletide traditions, Moore's image of Santa Claus created the foundation for the modern American version of Santa Claus. Moore's work was influenced by Washington Irving, who helped popularize St. Nicholas in the U.S. in his *A History of New York,* published on St. Nicholas Day in 1809.

In *'Twas the Night Before Christmas,* Santa became a round and jolly gift-giver with twinkling eyes and rosy cheeks. These images are now deeply embedded in Christmas mythology and forever entwined in children's imaginations.

'Twas the Night Before Christmas endures through the families who read it and make it a part of their own individual holiday traditions. The poem has been a seasonal favorite, enchanting children of all ages for almost 180 years.

CLEMENT C. MOORE

'Twas

THE NIGHT BEFORE CHRISTMAS

With Illustrations by
HADDON SUNDBLOM
AND
GARIN BAKER

'Twas

the night before Christmas,
when all through the house,
Not a creature was stirring,
not even a mouse.

The stockings were hung
by the chimney with care,
In hopes that St. Nicholas
soon would be there.

The children were nestled
all snug in their beds,

While visions of sugarplums
danced in their heads;

And Mama in her kerchief
and I in my cap,
Had just settled down
for a long winter's nap.

When out on the lawn
　　there arose such a clatter,
I sprang from the bed
　　to see what was the matter.

Away to the window
　　I flew like a flash,
Tore open the shutters,
　　and threw up the sash.

The moon, on the breast
of the new-fallen snow,
Gave the luster of midday
to objects below.

When, what to my wondering
eyes should appear,
But a miniature sleigh
and eight tiny reindeer,

With a little old driver
so lively and quick,
I knew in a moment
it must be St. Nick.

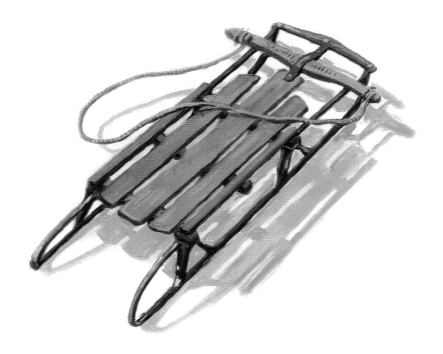

More rapid than eagles
   his coursers they came,
And he whistled, and shouted,
   and called them by name—

"Now, *Dasher!* Now, *Dancer!*
   Now, *Prancer* and *Vixen!*
On, *Comet!* On, *Cupid!*
   On, *Donder* and *Blitzen!*

"To the top of the porch!
   To the top of the wall!
Now dash away! Dash away!
   Dash away all!"

As dry leaves that before
the wild hurricane fly,
When they meet with an obstacle,
mount to the sky.

So up to the housetop
the coursers they flew,
With the sleigh full of toys,
and St. Nicholas too.

And then, in a twinkling,
    I heard on the roof
The prancing and pawing
    of each little hoof.

As I drew in my head
    and was turning around,
Down the chimney St. Nicholas
    came with a bound.

He was dressed all in fur,
   from his head to his foot,
And his clothes were all
   tarnished with ashes and soot.

A bundle of toys
   he had flung on his back,
And he looked like a peddler
   just opening his pack.

His eyes—how they twinkled!
  His dimples how merry!
His cheeks were like roses,
  his nose like a cherry!

His droll little mouth
  was drawn up like a bow,
And the beard on his chin
  was as white as the snow!

The stump of a pipe
  he held tight in his teeth,
And the smoke it encircled
  his head like a wreath.

He had a broad face
   and a little round belly
That shook when he laughed
   like a bowl full of jelly.

He was chubby and plump,
   a right jolly old elf,
And I laughed when I saw him,
   in spite of myself.

A wink of his eye
and a twist of his head,
Soon gave me to know
I had nothing to dread.

He spoke not a word,
but went straight to his work,
And filled all the stockings
then turned with a jerk.

And laying his finger
    aside of his nose,
And giving a nod,
    up the chimney he rose.

He sprang to his sleigh,
    to his team gave a whistle,
And away they all flew
    like the down of a thistle.

But I heard him exclaim
   as he drove out of sight,
"Merry Christmas to all,
   and to all a good night!"

FAVORITE HOLIDAY MEMORIES

Date

FAVORITE HOLIDAY MEMORIES

Date

FAVORITE HOLIDAY MEMORIES

Date

FAVORITE HOLIDAY MEMORIES

Date _____

_____

_____

_____

_____

_____

_____

_____

_____

_____

_____

_____

HADDON SUNDBLOM, 1961